NGORONGORO–

where cow
poo is lucky!

AIRMAIL FROM...

NGORONGORO –

where cow poo is lucky!

Michael Cox

Illustrated by
Rhian Nest James

Hippo

Scholastic Children's Books,
Commonwealth House, 1-19 New Oxford Street,
London WC1A 1NU, UK

A division of Scholastic Ltd
London ~ New York ~ Toronto ~ Sydney ~ Auckland
Mexico City ~ New Delhi ~ Hong Kong

Published in the UK by Scholastic Ltd, 1999

ISBN 0 590 66015 2

Typeset by M Rules
Printed by Cox & Wyman, Reading, Berks

2 4 6 8 10 9 7 5 3 1

Ngorongoro - where cow poo is lucky! is part of a series of books about fascinating countries around the world. Each book is made up of letters written by a boy or girl who lives in one of these countries. You might find that their English isn't always quite right (unlike yours, which is always perfect - ha ha!). So watch out for a few mistakes and crossings out. Sometimes in their letters the children use words from their own language (just like we all do!). If you come across one in this book and don't know what it means, look it up on pages 37-38.

The Swahili language has some words that are a real mouthful. There's no need to choke on them though! Tackle them in bite-size pieces, like this... Ng-oron-goro. The beginning of this name is like the 'ng' in sing - but please don't try to sing it!

3 July

Hello to you and greetings from Africa!

My name is Christopher ole Nerento and I am ten years old. I am one of a tribe, or group of people, called the Maasai and I live near the place called Ngorongoro in the country of Tanzania.

Just lately I have started going to school a bit. It is a very interesting thing to do isn't it? Listen - if you are not doing this thing already I think you must do. But maybe you are like me and cannot go often because you have to look after your father's cows?

school hurray!

mooo!

In my visits to school I have found out some things which have opened my eyes very wide! Our teacher, Mr Mulenga, has been telling us all about the other lands that are in the world and showing us pictures of big cities and towns full of ~~skyscrappers~~ skyscrapers, shopping palaces and roadways wider than a big river.

Beep beep!

road

Beep beep!

I'm lost!

GET OUT OF MY WAY!

Yoo hoo! I think there must be more people in these places than ants in an anthill!

Do you live in one? (I mean a city – not an anthill!) If you do live in a city I think you must have a most exciting life! Now that I know about these places I am very crazy to learn more about them and to talk to some of the children who live there. I would like to do this in a telephone but I have not got one. So instead I have decided to send you my letters. It is going to be my school writing project for nearly all of one year. Mr Mulenga says he thinks it is a very great idea! I know you will enjoy my writings because my English is very ~~gudd~~ good.

Listen – I will try to write to you on many days but if sometimes a letter is not coming, do not worry! Maybe I am busy helping my father . . . or my posting man has been eaten by a lion!

GRRRR!

GO AWAY! This is top important letter from Christopher!

Here for you is my copy of Mr Mulenga's world

picture map. So now you will know where I live. I have put a cross where my village is. Can you see your living place on the map?

Best wishes for now from your new African ~~meat~~ mate!

Christopher ole Nerento

PS I have an English word book to help me with my letters. It is quite a bit old and some pages are torn so if I am ~~crissing~~ crossing my words up a bit this may be why.

Also, what tribe do <u>you</u> belong to?

15 July

Dear new friend,

Supa! I greet you! How are you? Today I will tell you all about me to help you to make a picture of your new pal from Africa inside your head!

I am a ten years old boy and I am 1.6 metres. I think I am quite high next to children from other places, but for my tribe this is normal. We are all very tall. To show you, here is a picture of me and my teacher Mr Mulenga, who is NOT a Maasai!

Me →

Mr Mulenga, my favourite teacher and my only teacher!

My skin is very dark brown all over my body except for my hand palms which are a bit pink. My hair is tight and curly to the top of my head. The tops of my ears have got holes in them which were put there when I was eight years old. They are a decoration. I am not at all fat on my body and my muscles are very good in all places. I am a very fast runner and can leap as a high as an ~~envelope~~ antelope. My bottom two middle teeth are missing. They were knocked away by mother. This was done to me in case I get the bad illness thing called lockjaw and cannot open my mouth to eat. Instead I can eat through the gap and then I will not starve. It is the same for all the children in my tribe. Also, I think it looks very nice, don't you?

When I grow up I would like to own many cattle and be an important senior warrior in my tribe. I would also like to be a teacher or a ~~vegetarian~~ ~~veteran~~ animal doctor or a lawyer.

I am learning English very fast now, from my big big brother who is a businessman in the big town called Arusha and also from my school teacher. But it takes more than one hour walking from my house

Horrible hyena

to my school and I do not manage to go there every day.

Very frightened calf

My really big knowledge is about animals, especially cows. I also have a lot of wiseness about wild creatures too. How to know when the hyenas are about to attack our calves, how to spot the leopard's paw marks in the mud near my house, those sorts of things and much more.

In my next letter I will send you pictures of my family so that you will know more what we are all like. Now I must dash away from you. My mum is shouting for me to sort out a problem. She says that our goats have pulled all of her washing from its drying place and are chewing it to pieces. I think I am in big trouble because I was supposed to be keeping my eyes on the goats today. I guess I must now go and do some big shouting myself!

Hurrahs for now,

Christopher

munch munch!

yum yum!

PS A quick information about my name. My real Maasai one is Loipirri ole Nerento but Mr Spencer, the Bible teacher who sometimes visits my school, gave me my Christopher one. I think I will use that one in my letters so it will be more easy for you.

19 July

Dear friend from skyscraper land,

Hello and good morning! How are things doing for you?
Here are my family pictures. I hope you enjoy them.
I have drawn us all in our enkang – that is our
word for our village.

I must tell you straight away that I could not
fit everyone in my family group on this picture.
Altogether I have got four mothers. They are all
my dad's wives. Maasai men marry more than one
woman but the mums don't all live in the same
house. They've each got a house of their own
where they live with their own children. This is
good because my brothers and sisters are
altogether very many indeed.

My stomach Mum, Naomi

My Dad, Daudi

spear

ear decorations

her shaved head has sheep grease on it - it looks nice. She wears beads around her head

Oltripe - bead collar for ceremonies

arm bangles

Karasha (blue)

ankle bracelets

his Orinka (cattlestick) if cows wee on this it is lucky!

Karasha (red checked)

ankle bangles

bare feet - he is more comfortable like this - he is good at missing scorpions and thorns!

My little sister, Ntoke - eight years old - likes playing house and chasing games but also does milking cows work

My little brother, Kimoisa - six years old - likes to climb trees

wooden ear plugs

beads

Karasha (brown)

bracelets and bangles

nice bead jewellery on her head and neck

Karasha (brown)

My dog, Nipa - he sticks his tongue out a lot!

he is not big but VERY brave!

Toy jeep made from tinlids and boxes (I made it)

14

My big brother, Leipo - a junior warrior

feather headdress, hair in plaits with wool done by his friends, coloured with red ochre (mud from the earth)

buffalo skin shield

very sharp knife

body paint

smart trainers given to him by a tourist

My big big brother, Nakordo - in his town suit, he has been to buy cattle medicine in Arusha

smart briefcase full of presents I hope!

city shoes

spear

My three other Mums

Grandmother

Grandfather

Some of my other brothers and sisters

some of our goats and a cow

15

Do you think my big big brother looks nice in his city clothes or do you like better my warrior brother in his karasha and head dress? Our clothes are nice and loose because we live in a hot place and so we need many cool breezes colding down our skin. They are <u>much</u> more comfortable.

In the old days the Maasai people's name for the Europe tribe people in their suits and trousers was "Iloredaa enjekat". This means "the ones who keep their bad wind smells trapped inside their clothes". Do not worry! I will not call you this rude thing!

Bye for now,

Christopher ole Nerento

(who lets <u>his</u> bad wind smells be blown away by the breezes!)

23 July

Hello dear ilcore (friend),

Here is your news from Africa!
I have been to my school class
<u>again</u> today. That is 12 times
already this term. I am doing
well, aren't I?

At my school this morning there
were great excitements. Mr Mulenga said that
many children (and even some grown ups!) from other
places think that Africa is a country. He was
explaining that Africa is a <u>continent</u> when there was
much screaming and commotions from right outside the
classroom. We all jumped from our seats and ran to
the window. There was a very big troop of baboons
raiding our shamba (that's the little
vegetable garden next to school).

17

The horrible beasts were all rushing about and pulling up the plants and kicking the soil and barking and screeching and being very, very naughty indeed.

Now, I do not know if you have baboons in the forests where you live, but I can tell you they are very bad here. They are also often very fierce. Sometimes a gang of them will even attack a large animal like a leopard and kill it!

But our brave teacher picked up his big stick and chased them into the bush with many thwackings and much shouting. When he came back we gave him a big cheer. But Mr Mulenga told us to be quiet. He said that the continent of Africa is made from more than 50 very different countries and that we, Tanzania, and our neighbour, Kenya, are two of them. Other continents are Europe, with lots of countries, and America with a north bit and a south bit.

Later on he told us that we have got a line on the earth called the <u>equator</u> running quite near to us. A boy in our class called Kalimu said he did much walking about with his father's cattle and that he had never seen this equator line thing, although he was always much looking on the ground for snakes and scorpions that might bite his feet. Mr Mulenga said that the equator is not a <u>real</u> thing. It is in the imagination and is for dividing the top half of the world ball from the bottom half. Look on my map picture and you will see it.

equator

Tanzania

And now, so that you will maybe learn some more about my great country and have some fun I have made you . . . A QUIZ! Listen! It was very hard for me to make and Mr Mulenga had to help me a lot. I am very proud of it so please do it!! If you don't know the answer, have a fun and just guess it. Or ask one of your mums to see if she is brainy.

YOUR AFRICA AND TANZANIA QUIZ?
BY CHRISTOPHER

? ? ? ? ? ? ?

1) Is Africa:

a) the biggest continent in the world

b) the smallest

c) the second biggest?

It's a bit tricky isn't it?

2) Which of these countries are in Africa?

a) Kenya

b) Guinea

c) New Guinea

d) Mongolia

e) Mauritania

f) Mali

g) Zambia

A little clue - there are five of them!

3) Is Tanzania:

a) two times bigger than Britainland

b) half as big

c) four-and-a-half times bigger?

Go on, just guess it!

4) What is our capital city? Is it:

a) Dodoma

b) Dar es Salaam

c) Durban

d) Dallas?

It certainly begins with 'D'!

5) What is our national language? Is it:

a) English

b) Swahili

c) Zulu

d) Tanzanian?

6) How many people are there in Tanzania?

a) 5 million

b) 60 million

c) 28 million

7) What colour is our country flag?

a) red, orange and blue

b) green, yellow, black and blue

c) green and yellow

8) What is our weather like?

a) hot, no rain

b) cold in the winter and hot in the summer

c) wet sometimes and hot all year

9) Is Tanzania:

a) the third richest country in the world

b) the fifth poorest

c) the most poorest?

10) What is Tanzania's top tourist attraction?

a) food

b) wild animals

c) water sports

I hope you have done well. I will put the answers at the end of my next letter to you.

Best wishes,

Christopher

PS How many mothers have you got?

20 August

Hello there my friend – how is you?

I hope you are working really hard in your classroom. Getting good education is very important so please do not waste your time.

Actually I have not been to school for many days now. While you have been in your school increasing your cleverness, I have been out on the grasslands guarding our cows from wild beasts with my cattle stick and my spear.

This is because my brother Saroney (the son of one of my dad's other wives) has trod upon a big thorn. The hole has gone bad and he cannot walk well, so now I must take his place and drive our cows to new grass.

OW!

23

The grass near by has all been completely eaten by our animals and the wild creatures. All that is left is red dust. Even the grass in the new place is very tired because it is a long time since our rains have been.

This is me and Nipa guarding our cows

listening with ears up

very sharp spear

Can you see how watchful we are, not just snoozing under a shady tree! Guarding cows is very important and dangerous work for one ten year old boy and his small dog. There are many fierce creatures about who wish to eat them and if we lose just one cow we will be in <u>big</u> trouble. Also, at certain times, our big bulls like to fight each other. It is my job to stop this. Sometimes that is not too easy! Here is my picture of two of our bulls having a fight. Do your cattle have horns too?

Here are some prowling lions behind the big rocks. I did not really see them today but often they are around and I must watch for them at all times. Also notice the antelope and zebra that graze quite peacefully right by our cattle.

Our cows are <u>all things</u> to us. Maasai people always say, "God gave us cattle and grass. Without grass there are no cattle and without cattle there are no Maasai." So now you know why my job is very important! As you will see, also there are many, many cattles for me to watch, so it is good that I know all of their names and faces. I check them many times just like your teacher checks your class when you go on an outing to the bush.

Has your father got a lot of cows in the countryside somewhere? I am guessing that he has very many because I have been told that all people in Europe and America are very, very rich.

Now, please listen carefully! If you do have cows I have got some bad news for you. I must now tell you that they are not really <u>yours</u> but they are actually <u>ours</u>! I know this is true because my grandfather told me that a long time ago God gave all the cows in the whole world to the Maasai people. So please look after them carefully for us. Thank you.

By the way, when you are not doing your school work what job do you do? Here we get our first one as soon as we are five years old.

Ntoke helps my mother with milking, water fetching and cooking.

Ntoke helps with food

mum

Kimoisa with his favourite baby goat

Kimoisa looks after our flock of lambs and baby goats near the enkang. He has his own little stick to guard them.

It is his practice for

when he becomes big enough to be with the cattle. Here he is doing his work . . .

Just one more thing. My mother has told us that we will soon be moving our enkang. We must find a place where the grass is better.

Best greetings,

Christopher

PS I nearly forgot to ask you! Do you like riddles? We are quite mad about them here. Here is one for you to be puzzling. I hope it will give you much confusion.

Question: The two of us cross the wilderness without talking to each other. Who are we?

Answer: In my next letter!

ANSWERS TO
YOUR AFRICA AND TANZANIA QUIZ
BY CHRISTOPHER

1) c) Africa is the <u>second</u> biggest of the seven continents in the world.

2) a) b) e) f) g)

3) c) It is four-and-a-half times bigger than Britainland. (Like a big elephant to a little goat!) Yes, we are very big!

4) a) Our capital city is Dodoma: it used to be Dar es Salaam.

5) c) Our national language is Swahili but the people here talk in over 100 different languages (not <u>all</u> by each person though!). We learn English because it helps us to get on in the big wide world. How many tongues has <u>your</u> country got?

6) c) There are about 28 million peoples in Tanzania. A lot of them are in big towns so there is very much room in most of the other places. You can walk for many, many days and never hardly see another human person – just lots and lots of wild creatures.

7) b)

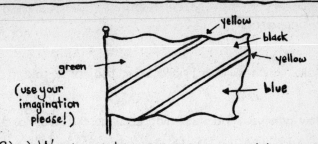

green
(use your imagination please!)

yellow
black
yellow
blue

8) c) We do not have a summer or a winter. Most of the time we just have hot weather in all places — but we do have snow on Mount Kilimanjaro <u>all</u> of the time. We also have two very rainy seasons. One long and the other short.

9) We are nothing like Europe and America with their factories and motorways. We are a "developing" country with mainly poor people doing farming and trying to make a better life.

10) b) of course!

How did you do? Not so good? Do not worry! Now you know some more about my country!

7 September

Hello there my rich friend from the north pole,

How are you? I am still not back to my school and
am busy doing much cattle guarding. While I have
been standing on the big grasslands for many hours
with the sky and Nipa and my cows for my company
I have been thinking of <u>you</u> in your big town.

What are you doing right at this minute? Are
you whizzing about in your motor car or are you
hitting your computer? No, of course you are not!
You are reading my letter (ha ha!).

Mr Mulenga says that often in your place of
living many times each day people are looking to
their watches and thinking, "Oh, oh, I am late for
this! Oh, I am late for that! Oh, look at this
traffic jam I am in. Whatever will I do?" Here in
Maasailand we do not rush about or look at our
watches a lot because many of us do not have
them. When we want to know where we are in

the day we just look at the place of the sun in the sky and then we know. And when we want to know where we are in the month we look at the moon shape. It is quite easy and not a bit worrying or hurrying. Why don't you try it?

School   Eat   Jobs to do

Time to wake up   my village   Bedtime

Today I drawed you this picture. It is of my stomach mum milking Mbilia who is <u>my</u> very own cow. Mbilia was given to me for being brave and not crying when I had the holes cut in my ear tops. I am very proud of her. She is my very favourite cow.

calf   mum
Mbilia

My mother is milking on one side and Mbilia's calf is drinking on the other, so that there are fair shares all round. My mums milk the cows every day. We save the milk inside our <u>il-kukurto</u> containers.

We use the milk for making sweet milky tea or

butter and just for drinking as it is. It has often got a smoky taste because we clean the inside of the il-kukurtos with hot charcoals.

Can you see Mbilia's bell? All of our cows wear different sounding bells on their necks so that if one is lost we will know where to find it (the cow, not the bell). We put marks on their bodies to say that they are ours.

In my next letter I will show you how Mbilia gives us fresh blood for drinking. Right now I feel quite sleepy from all my drawing and writing and guarding so I think I will go to my bed.

Goodnight sincerely,

Christopher

PS Answer to riddle: Me and <u>my shadow</u>. Ha ha!

8 September

Good morning my old ~~champ~~ chum,

How are you doing today? Are you feeling as fat as a fiddle? I am now as fresh as a daisy because I have had a big sleep and also a nice drink of cow's blood. Do you drink the cow's blood too? In case you don't, I have drawn you these pictures so that you will understand about it.

Dad shoots an arrow into the big blood vein in Mbilia's neck. Believe me or not she never complains and we know that it does not hurt.

This is the special arrow we use. This bit stops it going too far in.

The blood squirts from her neck and we catch it in our il-kukurto.

When we have got enough blood we plug up the

hole with a lump of cow poo mixed with some mud. This is to stop Mbilia's blood pouring out on the ground and killing her. Happily we drink the blood.

Cow poo

Yum yum

Sometimes we drink the blood on its own or sometimes mixed with cow's milk and sometimes we make it into special blood puddings. It makes us really, really strong.

I must tell you now that we hardly ever kill our cows for eating. They are far too important to us for that! Every while in a once we eat a cow at a special ceremony. Have you heard that in some places in the world the people kill many, many cows and sheeps and pigs? They fill up their shopping palaces with their meat pieces! Do you just use your cows for meat and milk or do you get lots of other things from them like we do?

We use our cows for money. When my mum married my dad his dad gave her dad some cows. This is called a "bride price".

Do you have money that walks around on four legs and says "Moo!"? Ha ha!

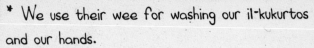

* We use their wee for washing our il-kukurtos and our hands.
* We use their dungs to build our houses with and to burn on our fires.
* We use their wee for going in our medicine.
* We use their skins for making sandals, ropes, bed covers and clothes.

So, now you can see our cows really are everything to us and we do not waste a thing.

My grandfather always says, "He who steps on cow poo does not die!" which means that if you have got cows you will always be OK. I think he is right. Best wishes,

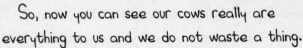

Oh what luck!

Christopher

PS Do your cows' backs have a big hump on them like ours? Our sort are called Zebu, what are yours called?

Also . . . here is another riddle for you.

Question: Empuru nemishu. Emodiei enkitang?

Answer: In my next letter!

15 September

Dear friendy pal,

Apayia enhorit! Have you noticed that just lately I have been putting some words in my letters that are from my speaking and not yours? I am sorry about this, sometimes it is hard for me to remember!

My language is called Maa. Maasai people talk with it but it is not the main big one for speaking in Tanzania. That one is called Swahili. Maasai people use some words from this language too. We hear it from many people and also on our radio.

I'm sending you a list of our words. I hope it will help you!

Best regardings,

Christopher

PS Last quick thing. I gave you the last letter riddle in my language. I am sorry for that. Here it is in English.

Question: It smokes but it is not lit. What is it?

Answer: Coming soon in a letter.

MY FRIEND PEN'S GUIDE TO MAA
by Christopher Ole Nerento

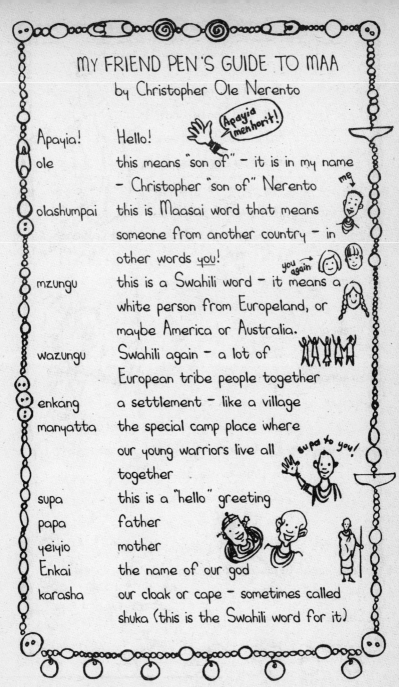

Apayia menhorit!

Apayia!	Hello!
ole	this means "son of" – it is in my name – Christopher "son of" Nerento
olashumpai	this is Maasai word that means someone from another country – in other words you!
mzungu	this is a Swahili word – it means a white person from Europeland, or maybe America or Australia.
wazungu	Swahili again – a lot of European tribe people together
enkang	a settlement – like a village
manyatta	the special camp place where our young warriors live all together
supa	this is a "hello" greeting
papa	father
yeiyio	mother
Enkai	the name of our god
karasha	our cloak or cape – sometimes called shuka (this is the Swahili word for it)

me

you again

supa to you!

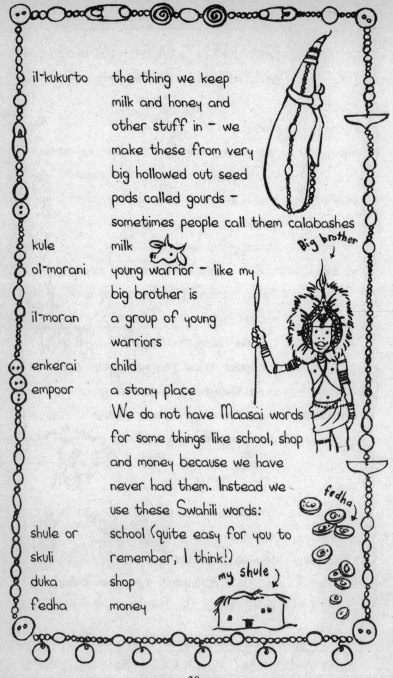

il-kukurto — the thing we keep milk and honey and other stuff in – we make these from very big hollowed out seed pods called gourds – sometimes people call them calabashes

kule — milk

Big brother

ol-morani — young warrior – like my big brother is

il-moran — a group of young warriors

enkerai — child

empoor — a stony place

We do not have Maasai words for some things like school, shop and money because we have never had them. Instead we use these Swahili words:

fedha

shule or skuli — school (quite easy for you to remember, I think!)

duka — shop

my shule

fedha — money

38

24 September

Good morning my olashumpai friend,

How are you today? I am in good spirits because we are now at our new place of living. Our cows are also happy because there is much sweet, thick grass here.

Altogether I think this will be a good place to be because we have the river close by and also a forest for medicine herbs and firewood. My warrior big brother will like this because he and his friends can wander about in there for many weeks having big adventures (I will tell you more about that later).

We are nearer to my school now so going there should be easier for me. As well, really close by, about half a day's walking, is a duka. Soon I will walk there. It is also the new place for posting my letters to you!

We travelled to our new living place with our

donkeys and cattle and goats and everything except our old houses. We left them behind us and have made new ones here. My mothers have just finished building them. It has taken them about six days and they are now ~~bushy buzzy~~ busy getting our lives back to normal.

Just in case you do not know how our houses are made, I have drawn you these pictures of my stomach mum making our new one and she has put her words with them. Perhaps you could show them to <u>your</u> mum, so that she will also know how to do this important woman's work.

*First the junior warriors cut down some young trees with nice, springy, bendy branches.

* I pushed these into the earth and bent their tops over to make a house shape and knitted them together with some grass stuck in too.

Poo! very smelly work!

*I got a big lot of wet, sticky cow poo and mixed it up with some mud, then spread it over the branches to make a thick wall. The hot sun baked the the dung very hard. Now it will not fall off and the smell will go away.

* At the front of the house I made a doorway and a tunnel to get inside.

* When we were finished building there were 25 new houses in our new enkang.

* The men made a big, thick wall of spiky branches, called an esita, all the way around them. In the evening we will bring our cattle inside it and pull extra branches across the gateway gap. This will protect them (and us!) from prowling wild animals.

not so smelly now!
It's looking good!

Some people say that our houses look like lying down elephants, or loaves of ~~bride~~ ~~bredd~~ bread? What do you think?

One other news. Saroney's foot is nearly better so soon I will go to my school again. Good!

Your best of friends,

Christopher

PS My little sisters made their own small pretendy house, copying my mums. It was good fun and also good practice for when they become mums. Later one of our cows put its foot on the new house and squashed it all completely flat (the toy one, not the real one!).

PPS Answer to my last riddle: fresh cow poo! Ha, ha!

29 September

Dear you,

Today I went all the way to Arusha on the back of my businessman brother's motorbike. He made it go very, very fast with very much loud screaming and roaring (from us _and_ the motorbike!). It was all very extremely exciting and quite a bit frightening – especially when we fell off. A big hole came into the middle of the road and suddenly we were lying in the dust and the naughty motorbike was carrying on to Arusha all on its own.

It soon got tired though and decided have a lie down too.

We were not too hurt, only a bit surprised and dusty, but the motorbike was badly hurt in its petrol squirter. It would not go any more. We sat by the side of the road and waited for a truck to come by and take us all to Arusha.

The big and busy city place was very interesting for me. There were hotels and jeeps full of touristers going on wildlife safaris.

Some of them were taking photographs of Maasai people who asked them for money and stood very still and fierce on the street while they did their snappings. I did not once see a Maasai person take a picture of a tourist though!

We visited some souvenir shop keepers. One day Nakordo will get a big truck of his own and drive around the enkangs. He will buy beautiful Maasai jewellery and spears and cattle sticks and things, and sell to the shops. The shops will sell them to the touristers. And Nakordo will get lots of money!

Nakordo went to see his girlyfriend who works in the market place, and then we rode back to our enkang. He did not go so fast this time and I was glad because just one crash was quite enough for me.

If you are not as rich as the wazungu, getting around the great big country of Tanzania is not easy. There are not a lot of roadways here and in our rainy season many of them are too wet and muddy for motor cars. In the dry season they are just dry and very dusty with potty holes and sharp pieces of stones that make tyres go bang!

Other times there are large, wild animals sitting in the middle of them!

I will tell you about all our different ways of travelling at the end of this letter.

Right now I am now going to inspect my body for broken parts!

Best wishes,

Christopher

PS How many kilometres do you walk to school?

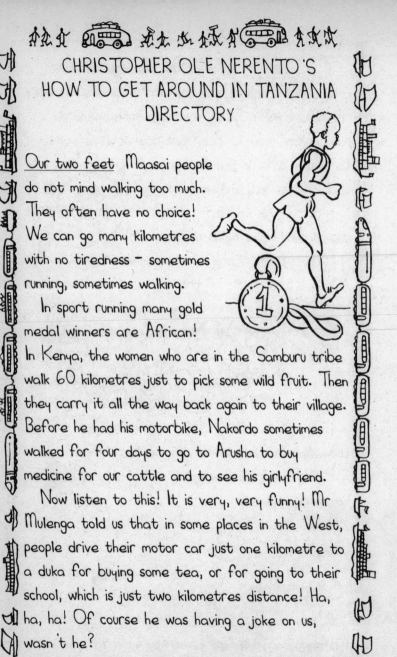

CHRISTOPHER OLE NERENTO'S HOW TO GET AROUND IN TANZANIA DIRECTORY

<u>Our two feet</u> Maasai people do not mind walking too much. They often have no choice! We can go many kilometres with no tiredness – sometimes running, sometimes walking.

In sport running many gold medal winners are African! In Kenya, the women who are in the Samburu tribe walk 60 kilometres just to pick some wild fruit. Then they carry it all the way back again to their village. Before he had his motorbike, Nakordo sometimes walked for four days to go to Arusha to buy medicine for our cattle and to see his girlyfriend.

Now listen to this! It is very, very funny! Mr Mulenga told us that in some places in the West, people drive their motor car just one kilometre to a duka for buying some tea, or for going to their school, which is just two kilometres distance! Ha, ha, ha! Of course he was having a joke on us, wasn't he?

<u>Our donkeys</u> We use these to carry our water and firewood and our things when we are moving to a new place. They are very strong and do not complain to us.

<u>Buses</u> Some buses have wooden seats and are hurtful to ride in when they bump around on the broken roads. They do not go until they are full up with people so often you have to wait a long time, or go looking for some extra passengers yourself!

You put your luggages on the roof. Sometimes also people travel on the roof, but this is not good when you are going fast round a bend or under some tree branches.

People take their animals on them so you might share your seat with a goat or a chicken!

<u>Dalla dalla</u> These are a sort of taxi – any

shape – maybe a car or maybe a truck. Often they break down so all of the passengers have to get out and push!

1, 2, 3, PUSH!

<u>Motor car</u> Sometimes these do not like our roads. The best sort for here are tough Ranger Rovers and such like. My grandfather will not ever go in a motor car, he does not like them at all! Many years ago he was given a ride in one. He said that the engine gases and the non-stop moving made him very poorly. Later on the car broke down and would not start up again. "There it was, dead in the road and we could not even <u>eat</u> it!" he said to me.

<u>Trains</u> These go big distances across Tanzania and do not break down quite so much.

You have to be careful on them as thieves sometimes jump through the windows and steal your things – so keep them shut with a piece of wood.

<u>Lake steamers</u> These go across our big lakes – some are very old. One was sunk but was brought up from the lake bottom and made to go again. There are big fights to get on the busy ones.

<u>Dhow</u> Arab sailing boats. These are blown along by the wind but now some have motors. Very nice to look at but no proper sleeping or sitting places when you are on them.

You might smell of fish when you have finished your dhow trip because fish oil is used to stop the boat wood from going rotten.

1 October

Hello there,

Are you busy at your home today – or are you taking some rest and putting your feet in the air while you watch your television ~~scream~~ screen?

When my stomach mum was making the porridge this morning I saw her trip over two times and also drop the cooking pot on her foot.

OOWW!

I thought that she looked very, very tired and felt much sorrow for her. I think that all the house building and walking and carrying took away many of her energies.

But there is no chance to rest now. Look! In her few spare minutes Mum and me have made you a ~~coffee table~~ timetable of her jobs with her words and my pictures and writing, so you will know about the many things she must do almost <u>every</u> single day of her life!

MUM'S TIMETABLE

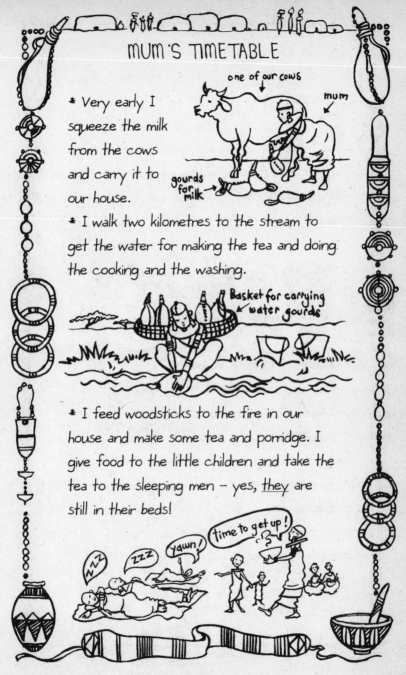

one of our cows

mum

* Very early I squeeze the milk from the cows and carry it to our house.

gourds for milk →

* I walk two kilometres to the stream to get the water for making the tea and doing the cooking and the washing.

Basket for carrying ← water gourds

* I feed woodsticks to the fire in our house and make some tea and porridge. I give food to the little children and take the tea to the sleeping men – yes, <u>they</u> are still in their beds!

ZZZ
zzz
yawn!
time to get up!

51

Cough! Cough!

* I take out the calves and the baby goats and sheep from our hut and sweep out the mess.

* I wash the little children, fetch more water, wash clothes and clean cooking pots.

splish, splash!

washing

clothes drying on rock

* I go to collect the firewood then chop it. I feed the fire many times.

chop! chop!

* I do more cooking and make more tea for the men when their friends arrive for talking.

making tea

Thirsty work this talking!

* I clean animal skins and peg them to dry in sun and sew beads on them for wearing.

drip drip!

* I pick gourds from tree vines and make into il-kurkurtos, then decorate them with beads and cow skin.

* Some days I do dipping the animals in chemical water to get rid of their fleas and ticks.

←fleas!

Of all my jobs I think the water fetching is the hardest! When it is done my back is always hurting. I am sure my arms have grown ten centimetres longer. Fill two of <u>your</u> bucket carriers with water and walk one kilometre with them — then you will know what I am talking about!

Is <u>your</u> mother's life like my mother's — with always work! work! work! — or does she have many machines to do her tasks for her?

When I am a grown up and have money from my top job I will buy my mum a clothes-washer machine. Maybe by then we will have some electricity to make it work. All she will have to do then is go to the river to collect the water to put in it!

Best wishes,

Christopher

PS I forgot to say to you that while my mother is doing all those different hard work things, the men are quite often sitting drinking their tea and having long talks and making big important decisions. I think that many Maasai men have quite a good life actually. I am glad I am a boy!

3 October

Hello my pal,

Just a shorty letter today as I am busy getting
ready to go back to my skuli!
   When I told Nakordo all about my house-building
letter to you, he said, "Christopher, you must tell
your letter friend that the Maasai are people
who want to stay with their old ways. That is why
we still build our houses this style. It is called
traditional! You must also tell them that all
African houses are not like this! We do not want
them to think that African people just live in
houses like the ones of the Maasai. Let them
know that many people in Africa also live in houses
just like Europe ones, with two levels and windows
and things. In many places there are cities with
freeways and office tower blocks, computers and
movie houses!"

He also said that I must tell you that as well we have Maasai people who are teachers, doctors, computer operators and lawyers. We are not <u>all</u> cattle herders you know!

So that is why I am sending you this letter. I do not want you to think that everyone here is living in the old times!

Lullabye bye,

Christopher

PS Nakordo is very pleased that I am wanting to be a teacher or an animal doctor. He says that the Maasai must keep some tradition, but also move with the times and get other bits modern really fast or we will be left with nothing! I think he is right!

4 October

Greetings to you old friend!

Today I have got much exciting news for you to eat! This morning, as I was going on my new way to school I had a most narrow escape! Listen! – this is what happened . . .

After three kilometres of walking, I had a meeting which I wasn't expecting. In some trees ahead of me there was a big dark shape. As I got near to it, I could see that it was a buffalo. It was not with any other buffalo like they often normally are. So it was a lone bull away from his herd. In other words, the most dangerous sort to meet when you are all on your own in the bush! This is what he looked like . . .

Here I must tell you that there are many, many buffalo in my place of living. Some are in the forests and some are on the savannah grasslands, often all in one herd with as many as 2,000 all together. They are a very big animal, up to

800kg heavy, almost as much as a small jeep! For the human being they are the <u>most dangerous</u> of all the beasts, much more dangerous than a lion or a rhino! If they are angry they will want to kill you and may chase you for many, many miles to do this.

My grandfather has told me stories of buffalo following the smell of wounded warriors for days so that they may catch them and kill them. Once he saw six buffalo fight a lion and kill it. He says it was a very amazing and terrible thing to watch that he will never forget.

All these things I was thinking when I watched the big buffalo who was also watching me!

me, very scared

Very angry buffalo

snort

He looked very old with many scars from fighting and was snorting and pawing on the ground. His big hooves made the red dust come up as he stared at me with his wicked eyes. I think he was very angry with me for stopping his peaceful snoozing. At that moment he put down his head and charged!

Now, as I have told you, I am a very good runner, so I didn't wait about. I turned and speeded off for the rock pile in the distance.

<u>But</u>, after only a few seconds I dropped my school exercising book.

my life-saving book

And the exercising book saved my life! I thought to myself, "Oh no! What will Mr Mulenga say if I come to school without my exercising book!" So, believe me or not, I stopped to pick it up! And I saw from my eye corner the buffalo go thundering right past me! He missed me!

Phew! Missed me!

I ran to a big anthill. When he stopped and turned to charge at me again I was right up on the top of it. The buffalo was grunting and beating the hill with his horns to make me to fall down so he could squash me. But, lucky me, a big group of warriors came along and chased him away with much shouting and throwing of rocks.

I was very late for school, so I ran all the way at very great speed. When I got there I was very hot and tired. Outside the school room Mr Mulenga was talking to the class in his stern voice. I began to feel very discomfortable indeed.

When I walked into the room everything went completely quiet and Mr Mulenga turned to me with very fierce eyes - just exactly like that old buffalo's! Also everyone else was staring to me too. I was sweating much and dusty and I had my torn exercising book in my hand and felt most ~~unbarrassed~~ embarrassed all over.

"You are late for school, Christopher!" said Mr Mulenga. "Why is this? Did you have some sort of a problem this morning?"

"Yes, I did Mr Mulenga," I said. "I was attacked by an old bull buffalo which nearly caught me, but I managed to climb on to an anthill and some warriors came by and rescued me!"

"And are there ants in your pants to show your story is true?" said Mr Mulenga. "Ha ha ha! Oh well, that is all right then. Take your place and open your book at page 52." And then he carried on with the lesson.

I will be more careful and watchful on my way to school tomorrow.

Best wishes,

Christopher

PS I must tell you that "eating the news" is what Maasai people say for when they are hearing new things (so please do not chew up my letters, ha ha!).

14 October

Dear friend,

Hello and good afternoon to you! What have you been doing at <u>your</u> skuli today? In <u>my</u> skuli we were talking about the old days of my country. Did you know that about 200 years ago many white people from places like Britain and France and Germanyland came to the African continent and took many of the countries away from the African people?

In class we did writings and map drawings about how this thing happened and I got ten out of nine marks for mine. I am so proud of it that I have made you this copy from my exercising book. Please read it (or I will send my warrior brother to chase you around your town — ha ha, only joking!).

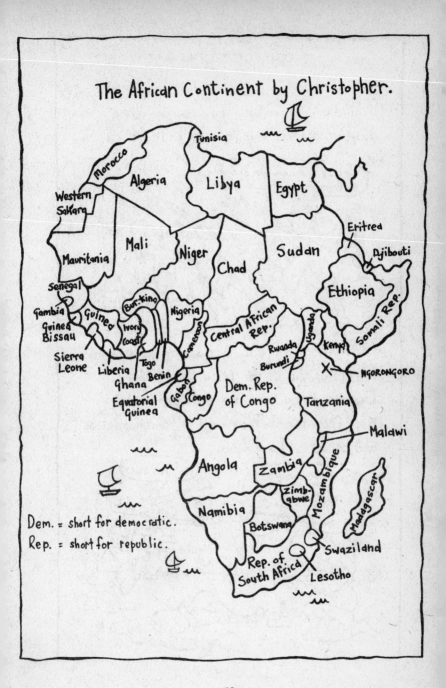

The African Continent by Christopher.

Dem. = short for democratic.
Rep. = short for republic.

PROJECT HEADING

In the 19th century the Germany tribe people took over this part of East Africa.

But then in Great World War One (1914-1918) the British tribe fought the Germany tribe here and took <u>our</u> country back from <u>them</u>! They kept it for themselves and called it Tanganyika.

In 1961 the British tribe gave Tanganyika back to the African people who re-named it Tanzania and joined it to the island of Zanzibar. This was called getting our <u>Independence</u>.

9/10 Well Done Christopher — a good piece of work. Mr Mulenga.

Sometimes there was much falling out between the African people and the Europe people. My grandfather told me that when he was a young warrior he was once put in a prison for stealing cows from a white man's farm. He and some other warriors went in the night and took them away.

When he was caught, he said to the policemen, "We were not stealing, God gave all the cattle in the world to the Maasai. We were only taking what was ours. Anyway, the farmland belonged to us before the white man took it and drove us away with his guns!"

I think he was right you know.

Peace and good happenings to you,

Your best friend,

Christopher

19 October

Dear Olushumpai,

The other day a new boy came to my school. At first he was showing off quite a lot and boasting about how strong and brave he was. This made me annoyed and soon we were having a pushing and pulling argument and then doing much rolling around in the dirt with ferocious wrestling.

Mr Mulenga ran out to us and lifted us into the air with our ears. He said we were very naughty and made us stay in at playing time. After this we became friends. The boy is quite nice really and his name is Sammy. He is not from the Maasai people, he is from the Swahili people and his mum and dad are the new owners of the duka. I will see him when I post my letters to you.

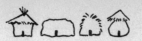

Sometimes in the old days different Tanzanian tribe people were often fighting with one another, but now it is OK and they all live very peacefully with each other (just exactly like me and Sammy!). Did you know we have more than 100 different sorts of tribes here! I cannot write about them all for you so I will just tell you about a few. Here they are:

CHRISTOPHER'S TANZANIAN TRIBE GUIDE

<u>The Maasai</u> Yes, this is my tribe, which I think you are finding much about already – I hope! Our old place of living was called Maasailand but it was broken in two by the Europe tribes. Now we live in two countries: Kenya and Tanzania.

Lake Victoria KENYA
MAASAI LAND
TANZANIA

<u>The Chagga</u> These people live on the side of the great big mountain called Kilimanjaro. They make houses from sticks and grass.

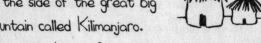
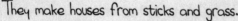

They are very clever at making water go uphill for bringing water to their crops. They grow things like the mbege plant (for beer) and coffee bean bushes (for coffee). They also carry the luggage and show the tourist people the way to the top of Kilimanjaro.

The Sukuma This is a very big tribe in Tanzania. They do much dancing and music playing and also can do snake charming. In one of their dances called the Ngama they dance with a living snake — a huge python or one like that — wrapped around the head and shoulders of their body!

The Hehe It is told that these people got their name because, "he he" is what they shouted as they went into battle.

HE HE!   HE HE!

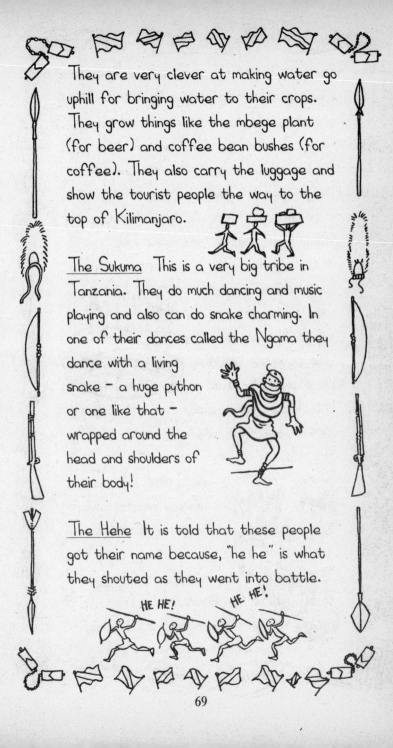

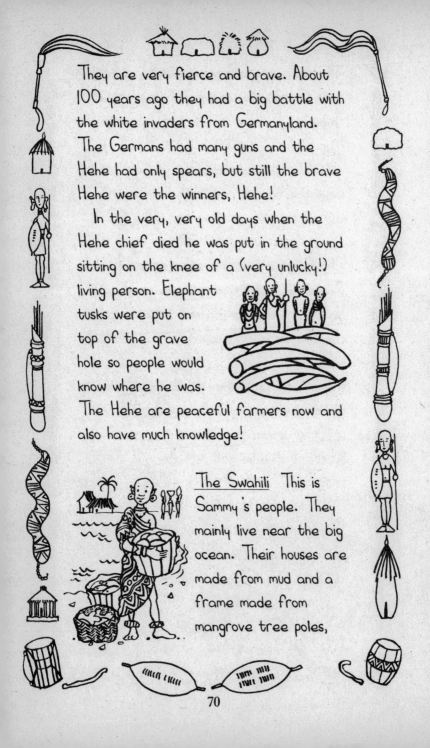

They are very fierce and brave. About 100 years ago they had a big battle with the white invaders from Germanyland. The Germans had many guns and the Hehe had only spears, but still the brave Hehe were the winners, Hehe!

In the very, very old days when the Hehe chief died he was put in the ground sitting on the knee of a (very unlucky!) living person. Elephant tusks were put on top of the grave hole so people would know where he was. The Hehe are peaceful farmers now and also have much knowledge!

<u>The Swahili</u> This is Sammy's people. They mainly live near the big ocean. Their houses are made from mud and a frame made from mangrove tree poles,

with roofs of palm tree leaves. They have been traders and fishermen for hundreds of years.

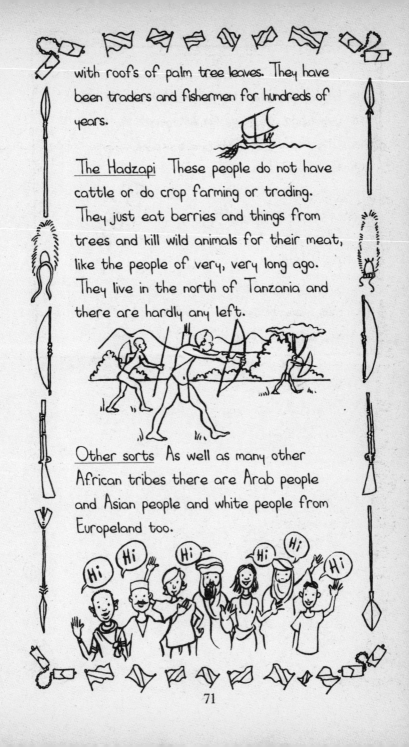

The Hadzapi These people do not have cattle or do crop farming or trading. They just eat berries and things from trees and kill wild animals for their meat, like the people of very, very long ago. They live in the north of Tanzania and there are hardly any left.

Other sorts As well as many other African tribes there are Arab people and Asian people and white people from Europeland too.

I think I must stop writing now. It is dark and the mosquitoes are starting to bite at me so I must go inside my house to escape from them. At least there are only flies and nasty insects called jiggers in there!

Best luck and good night,

Christopher

PS How many tribes do you have in your country?

21 December

Dear friend in the crowded place,

How are you doing? Are your parents and your brothers and sisters with you at your home or are they all busy racing from this place to that place?

Leipo, my big brother, is 19. He is back to see us here at our new enkang. He is here for just a short time and then he will rejoin his junior warrior age group back in their manyatta. In the forest they are learning their traditional Maasai warrior skills. So that you will understand more about what goes on I have made this picture of him and his warrior brothers. I hope you enjoy it!

Being brave and cunning fighters

Knowing about roots and herbs that cure illness

Doing each others' special warrior hairstyles and body painting

Learning the ways of the wild animals

Practising to throw spears well

Getting to be good at wrestling

and also — if it was still in the old days — fighting a lion to prove their courage

Lion fighting does not happen any more, because the law of my country does not allow it. Being a warrior is still very important.

When my grandfather was a young man it was even more important. In those times it was very needed to have a group of fearless young men to protect everyone else from wild animals and other tribes. And to go off on cow-stealing raids so that we would always have plenty. The warriors were very respected people and still are, and we must all show great politeness to them. We children are not allowed to see them eating and also they must not eat meat that has been touched or cooked or even looked at by a woman.

If we see the warrior spear sticking in the ground outside the house it means we may not enter.

When I am a few years older I will become a junior warrior and will have a special ceremony where my face will be  painted. I also will then go off into the forest and learn our traditions with a group of boys who are all nearly my age. I am a bit worried about this. I think it will be quite hard for me to learn the traditional Maasai ways <u>and</u> learn the knowledge and ways of the big world. They are very different. Even so I will still try very hard to do both of them. My brother says he really would like to fight a lion, but he knows this is now against the law so he has to be happy with wrestling his friends.

In a few months he will no longer be one of the junior warriors and he will become a senior warrior at a special ceremony called Eunoto. Now he is thinking that his adventure days are almost at an end. When this happens he wants to get some work with the poacher-catching patrol and help to protect our wild lifes from the bad men who kill them for their skins and horns. In that way he will get to taste some action and perhaps also show his great bravery.

How do you prove yourself to be brave and learn about your traditions where you are?

Besty wishes,

Christopher

PS In my next letter I will tell you my grandfather's story of the day <u>he</u> killed a lion. Do you have fierce young warriors in your town or village?

Fierce look-
are you
scared?

22 December

Hello there - ~~who~~ how are you?

Have you had an exciting day today or done something that took much courage? The other evening when the other children and me were sitting by the fire with our  grandfather, I told him about our big brother's wish to fight a lion. This put grandfather's thinking back to his own warrior days many, many years ago and soon he began singing to us.

Singing is what many of our old people do when they want to tell a story. Grandfather's song was about the day he first came face to face with a lion. This is what he sang:

"I was about 18 years old and I had done many things: cattle raiding, protecting our water places from our enemies, all sorts! I knew the time would soon come when I would have to face the final big

77

test that all young moran go through to prove themselves a true warrior – the one that is harder than all others – to fight a lion! Even now,

GRRRR!

all these years on I can still remember how I looked forward to it. I couldn't wait!

At around this time we knew of a lion with a black mane that was quite near by to our enkang and was giving much trouble. It had eaten two of our cows, and killed one of our donkeys.

One day my brother brought us news that this same lion had now become a man-eater. Some white men had been camping not far from our enkang. One of them had left his tent open to keep cool and had fallen asleep with his head sticking outside.

ZZZZZ

In the middle of the night the lion had picked him up by his head and carried him off into the forest! His screams woke up his friends. They followed the lion into the bush.

They fired their guns at the lion so it dropped

their friend and ran off. But it was too late. He was already completely dead. When we heard this news we knew it was time for a lion hunt.

We left our camp and went deep into the forest, where we made our preparations. We covered ourselves in red ochre grease and plaited our hair using woollen threads. Next we tied bells to our legs and put on finest head dresses. Lastly we cooked a soup of forest plants which we ate to give us courage for the coming battle. We were now ready for the hunt!

Seizing our spears and shields we went off to the place where the lion had been seen. We quickly found its trail and knew that we would catch up with it soon so we stopped to stuff grass leaves inside our bells so he would not hear their jingling.

After some more running our leader found some droppings on the track and examined them. They were fresh and still a little bit warm. They were from the lion! Minutes later we heard a roar in the bushes ahead of us. The lion had seen us and was running away! The chase was on! We pulled the grass from our bells and ran after him, chanting and stamping and jangling our bells as we did. It was all really thrilling!

At last, the lion decided to stand and fight. He was enormous with fierce, flashing eyes and very big, black hair! We made a circle around him and began to close in.

I asked myself who would he choose to attack? I knew the answer. The first moran to lower his shield would be the one that the lion attacked. I was that warrior!

We slowly moved towards the snarling lion, all the time chanting and making the circle smaller and

w hooosh!

smaller! I lowered my shield, got ready to throw my spear and the lion leapt at me. I hurled my spear with all my strength, but the lion's huge claws sank into my shoulder. Its roaring was deafening and I could smell its hot meaty breath on my face and feel the fire of its claws deep in my flesh!

Just as I was expecting its teeth to sink right inside my throat the lion fell away from me, spitting and snarling. Six or seven of my brother warriors' spears were sticking in his body. A second later, he was dead! I was a hero. I had proved my bravery.

Later on, after my brother warriors had put hot fire ashes on my wounds to stop them from going bad, we marched from one village to another singing about our great success. Everyone came out of their houses to praise us for our courage. We were all heroes and I will never forget that day.

OUR HEROES!

Well done boys

After his story my grandfather showed us the big scar places where the lion's claws had ripped his flesh and all the little children said, "Ooh!" and "Aargh!" Then he went into his house and fetched out a magnificent lion's mane head dress. It was the hair of the lion he had killed all those years ago!

Grandfather's lion's mane headdress shows everyone how brave he is

Even though grandfather has sung us the story of that lion hunt many times before I really enjoyed it. I never get tired of hearing of his adventures!

Best wishes,

Christopher

PS How do you pass on the old stories of your tribe? Do your grandparents sing them to you or are they told to you by your television machines?

2 January

Dear pal who reads my letters,

I hope you are OK and having much luck in your life. Here we have settled to our new houses and everything is well. After I was telling you about the building of the houses I suddenly thought you should know about the inside. So in this letter I am going to take you on a guided safari tour inside my house. Follow me please! It will not take us too long because it is only small!

I think maybe you do not live in houses made from cow dung. Do you have the double layer house with stairs in between the top and bottom? Also in a book at school I have seen a picture of a moving staircase — have you got one of these in your house?

Best wishes,

Christopher

It is going too fast!

It will not stop. HELP!

But here is some tea.

PS Nakordo has got his truck. It is quite old and green coloured with red and yellow side pieces. It makes lots of smoke when he drives it but he is most proud!

Our House

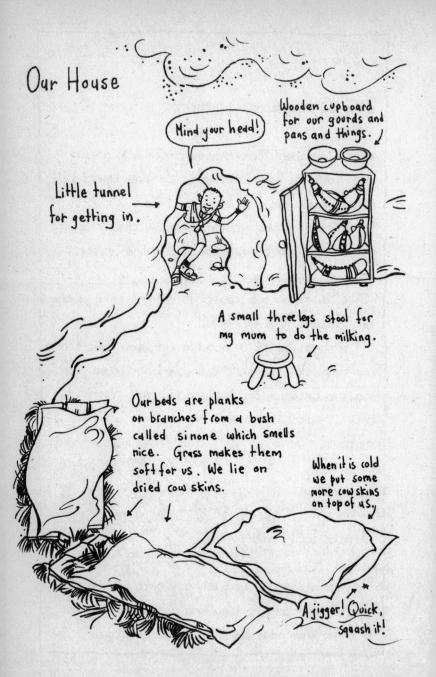

Olale — a small animal-keeping space. You may not see it at first because our houses are very dark inside. No window holes! Take time to get used to the dark.

We keep our newborn animals here for some days so they get to know us. Sometimes they moo and bleat when I am in bed. Do you keep your cows in your house?

Fire woods and fireplace made from three stones from the river. We burn wood between the stones. It is smoking most of the time so it will sting your eyes a bit at first.

We are also a bit dusty in the air because our floor is made from dry soil plus some animal messes. We sprinkle water on the dusts to stop them going in our eyes.

My bed
(very comfortable)

6 February

Supa and "Hello to you!".

I am really itching to tell you the great fun that I had yesterday. I did not go to school! Instead, I went into the forest to gather honey with my Uncle Meroki and Nipa. Uncle is an expert at finding the bees' nests and collecting their honey.

Honey is very special to Maasai people. Remember, we do not have shopping palaces for buying candy and sweety things as many other people. Honey is a real treat for everyone, especially the little children.

My uncle also likes to make honey beer which he enjoys to drink with the senior elders.

When we got into the forest the light was flickery and spotty like a cheetah skin and there were many butterflies and birds flittering through the leafy ceiling. As we walked along the trail we could hear the chatter of the insects and also the scream of the baboons and the bark of the  leopard. Whenever this happened the hairs on Nipa's back stood up and he curled his lips and growled bravely.

Soon we reached the place that Uncle was looking for. "Now, here is the tree," he said. "Look, the nest is in that fork of the branches."

He took out his olpiron (fire sticks) and began to work them. He twirled the sticks. Thin whisperings of smoke came from the grass and then a glow came on it.

When he blew on this, small flames flickered up which he put twigs on to make the fire grow big, while I gathered more wood. Soon we had a big fire blazing fiercely, with the smoke going up to

the nest and making the bees fly away. When it
looked like most of them were gone, Uncle put a
big branch from the forest floor against the tree
trunk for a ladder, then said, "You keep watch for
buffalo and leopards while I get the honeycomb."

Here is my picture of
him going up the tree. It
was a high up place to go,
wasn't it?

When Uncle reached
the nest, he pulled his
karasha blanket over his
head and shoulders to
protect himself from
leftover bees. Then,
without fear, he pushed his
hand deep inside it and
pulled out large pieces of
honeycomb and put them in his gourds.

Be careful Uncle!

woof

When he had got as much as he could carry, he
came down and handed me a piece. I sucked some
honey from it and it was delicious! I even let Nipa
have a lick from my hand, but I didn't let Uncle
see me do this. Suddenly I felt sharp pain on my
bottom and then another on my arm . . . then

another . . . then another! It was the bees! Now
that the smoke was nearly finished they were
coming back to their nest. They were very angry
and they wanted to tell us about it!

"Hmm," said Uncle, licking his fingers and knocking
some bees from his face. "It's time for us to go!"

"Snarrgh . . . Grrr . . . Grrr!" said Nipa as he
snapped at the bees.

"Ooh, oww!" I said — but very quietly.

When we got back to our enkang we were very
tired and hurting after our day's work, but
everyone was pleased to see us and they were
very happy with the honey. Soon the little children
were asking for more, while the old men filled
their beer-making gourds with sticky syrup.

"Well, at least we got good honey!" said Uncle as we covered our stings in sheep fat to make them better.

Those bee stings are still hurting today, but I have not cried once, not one bit! For Maasai that sort of thing is only for <u>very little children</u> – no one else at all!

Best wishes,

Christopher

best
cow

PS I hope your cattle are all well.

24 March

Hello my chum!

Are you doing well? How is your weather? Are your rivers just empty beds or are they rushing with flood waters? Here we had the first of our long rains last night. This is good because the river is filling and soon the grass will grow thick and tall for our cows. So we are all quite happy.

Some things else that are happy and excited about all the wetness are the insects. Outside my house last night, there were many large clouds of moths and beetles flying in the air. Today when I was taking our cows to the grass I saw soldier ants and creeping things under my feets everywhere.

Just so you will know some of the many insects we share our country with I have made you this

guide. Read it and you'll see that Tanzania's big animals aren't the only amazing sort!

TANZANIAN INSECTS

<u>Termites</u> Some people call them white ants. Watch out for their houses on the savannah, they are in many places and can be useful at times (especially when you are being chased by a mad buffalo, ha ha!). Some are three metres tall! (the houses, not the insects). The giant queen termite spends her whole life being looked after by worker and soldier termites and laying one new egg every minute! Some people in Tanzania eat termites by frying them in butter. Termites eat all wooden things, even whole houses, but <u>not</u> fried in butter. All they leave is the paint — really!

<u>Soldier ants</u> I have seen an army of these marching across the grass hundreds of metres long and I have seen them attacking much bigger animals

like even frogs! They bite them to knock them
out and then they eat them. One time I was
attacked by some soldier ants and their stings
gave me <u>very</u> great pain indeed (but luckily they
didn't bother to eat me, ha ha!).

<u>Dung beetles</u> After the rain the female ones roll
up buffalo and elephant poo into big balls, larger
than themselves. They bury the ball, then lay

their eggs inside it. This is to
give their children something to
eat when they hatch out (yum
yum!). Sometimes on wet nights
the ground is covered in a
carpet of them all busy rolling their dung balls. It
looks just like an enormous football training session!

<u>Giant Millipede</u> This is up to
30 centimetres long, very
shiny black with many, many,
many red legs. People call it
the Tanganyika railway. Guess
why! Don't worry, it won't bite!

<u>Scorpions</u> There are big ones of these in dry bush

country. Some are as long as 20 centimetres (almost as long as this letter!) Be careful where you put your feet because their sting will make a big and hurty lump in your flesh! And sometimes it can make you die, (but this is rare).

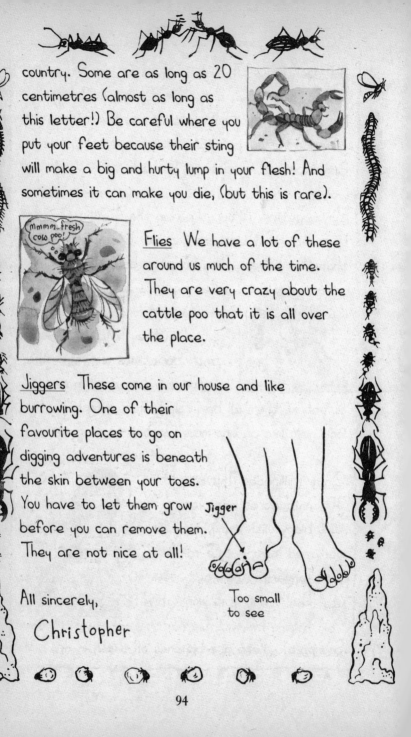

mmm...fresh cow poo!

<u>Flies</u> We have a lot of these around us much of the time. They are very crazy about the cattle poo that it is all over the place.

<u>Jiggers</u> These come in our house and like burrowing. One of their favourite places to go on digging adventures is beneath the skin between your toes. You have to let them grow before you can remove them. They are not nice at all!

Jigger

Too small to see

All sincerely,

Christopher

3 May

Dear old friend,

Best wishes from Tanzania! I am sorry I have not lettered you for a big time. I have been greatly busy with much walking and working. I will try to be sorry for this by doing many extra writes to you in the next days coming. My year of letters to you will be finishing to its end in just some weeks from now, so I will be extra tryful to do this!

Today my letter is not from my enkang. Instead it is from a wazungu safari camping place on the great big Serengeti plains!

I have not been to my school for some days now because I am with my father on the Safari Trek. I am helping him with his tourist guiding work. I do not feel bad about missing my lessons because

some time ago the big winds blew the roof off our classroom and the wall fell down on Mr Mulenga's head. It was much eaten by white ants and very rotted away - the wall, _not_ his head! Anyway, my school is now closed for a short time.

On the safari I have got the job of extra helper. I am carrying and fetching water and making fires and pot cleaning and helping to feed the safari touristers.

They have come to look at and shoot the many amazing animals of the Serengeti, but only with their cameras (gun shooting was just mainly in the old days!).

I am having a really good time and learning much about the peculiar behaviours of the strange creatures. The wild animals are also very interesting too - ha ha - only my joke! Actually, the wazungu are mainly quite nice and polite to us.

There is just one man and his wife who have many, many cameras around their necks and much flesh on their stomach and bottoms. They are always quite bossy to us and say many times to me, "Stand there with your spear! We want to take your photograph next to the zebras!" and things like that.

They also ask many stupid questions. Yesterday the woman mzungu pointed to an elephant, then said to my father, "Is that elephant an African or an Indian one?"

"It is an African one, madam," said my father. "They are the only sort we have got."

Then he said quietly to me, "Does she think the other kind swim across here from Indialand or something? Hmmph!"

One big thing the wazungu have come to see is the enormous moving of the wildebeest antelope across the

Serengeti.

It is an odd creature - we say that god made it from the bits that were left over when he had finished making all the other animals. Ha ha, another joke!

At this time of year, thousands and thousands of these big antelopes gather together to move to better grass in the north. There are so many of them it looks like all the Serengeti is painted black with them! It is called the "migration".

The lions and leopards and cheetahs and wild dogs are following the wildebeest - they have to . . . their <u>dinner</u> is on the move!

While they are moving, wildebeest life goes on. The bull wildebeest are fighting over their wives.

The wives are having calves. And the lions and leopards and cheetahs are hunting whatever they can catch. Many antelope and zebra are moving with the herd for new grass. And we are moving behind in jeeps and mini-buses.

The touristers have something to watch all day. Even at night when they sit around the camp fire they can hear the screams and roars of the animals close by in the bush. Would you like to be doing this? I think you would enjoy it very much if you did. I must stop writing now. My father is calling me to carry the touristers to their dinners!

Best wishes,

Christopher

5 May

Dear friendy pal,

How are you? Today I have got somethings to tell you which will make you laugh your head in! Last night while the bossy mzungu man and woman were asleep my father creeped to their resting place and pressed pretend lion's paw prints in the mud with his two fists. Then he did his pretend lion roaring (he is very good at this).

This morning when the woman came from her sleeping bag, she told us that a lion in the night had made her jump completely from her skin. When she saw the tracks near her doorway, she shouted,

EEEEK!

"Oh no! A lion was creeping around our t . . . t . . . tent last night!! We m . . . m . . . might have been eaten up while we were sleeping!"

My father and I were soon crying from laughing so much.

Later on her husband was taken prisoner by a "wait a bit" bush. He was hiding behind it to go to the toilet. This bush has very special thorns that hook your clothing very easily. When you are caught, the more you jump about to escape the more you are trapped! That is why it is called the "wait a bit" bush.

The man did a lot of jumping and a lot of shouting and could not escape at all!

My father found him and had to cut his clothes free with his knife. It is lucky a hungry lion did not find him!

Our safari work will finish soon. When it does I will be a little bit sad but also a little bit happy. One day you must come to Tanzania and see the amazing wildebeest migration sight for yourself! Just so you will know what you are seeing when you do come I have made you this guide to help you know more about some of our many great animals. I also have put some safety tippings (STs) with it so you will not be eaten. I hope you enjoy it!

ANIMAL SPOTTING GUIDE TO USE ON YOUR TANZANIAN SAFARI

Lion

Lions hunt in their group with the lionesses doing the running and the most work (like my mums). When the kill is caught the men lions get to eat first. The women have to wait their turn (a bit like my mums also). Lion cubs have spots, but these go away when they get big.

A lion's roar is very loud (I heard them from my bed last night). The air vibrations that come from roaring lions' mouths are so strong that they can make the dust fly up two metres away! Lions wee on the ground to make a "keep away" smell sign for their territory.

Cheetah

This Cheetah is not as strong as the lion or the leopard but is very fast – the fastest running animal in the whole world! It trips up the animal it is chasing then kills it.

Leopard

These are even more dangerous than lions and cheetahs. They do their moving at night and sleep in trees in the daytime. Sometimes they jump on to a gazelle deer from a tree then carry it up into the branches to eat it — they are very strong! So do not climb a tree to escape from them.

You will be just wasting your time! <u>ST</u> Big cats — If they come near to you and look like they are going to jump on you, stand still and make a lot of horrible noise to make them think you are fiercer than them.

Impala

These antelopes are eaten by leopards (if they can catch them!). They are great jumpers. They could leap over me sitting on my big brother's shoulders and still not even touch the top of my head! They can also leap right the way across a two lane road – that's ten metres! I wish I could do that sort of jumping!

Giraffe

Mr Mulenga says these are the tallest animals in all the world and that they are higher than a London deck-doubler bus! They grow up to five-and-a-half metres high. A new baby one is nearly as high as me as soon it is born! There are quite a lot of different sorts in Africa but in Tanzania we have only one, the Maasai giraffe (of course!). Its picture is the national badge of Tanzania.

Elephant

When they flap their ears they are trying to get cool. If their ears stand straight out stiff from

their head, watch out – maybe they are going to attack you!

Even though they are big they can move very quietly and may come up behind you and give you a big surprise. They have bad eyes but good smelling.

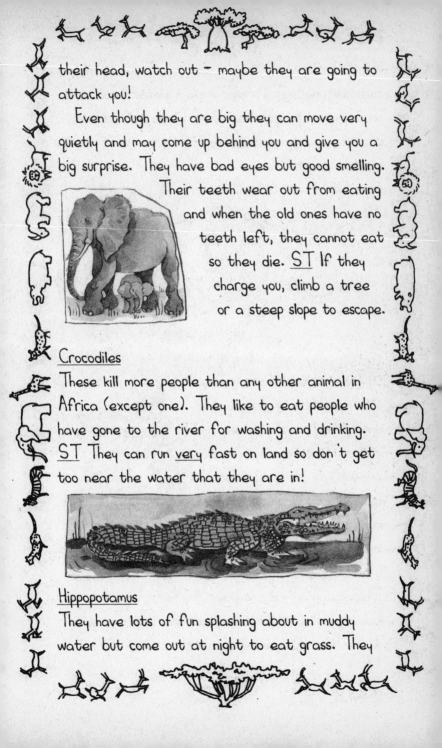

Their teeth wear out from eating and when the old ones have no teeth left, they cannot eat so they die. <u>ST</u> If they charge you, climb a tree or a steep slope to escape.

Crocodiles

These kill more people than any other animal in Africa (except one). They like to eat people who have gone to the river for washing and drinking. <u>ST</u> They can run <u>very</u> fast on land so don't get too near the water that they are in!

Hippopotamus

They have lots of fun splashing about in muddy water but come out at night to eat grass. They can hold their breath and go for a walk about on the river bottom for six whole minutes! Lions and crocodiles eat hippo babies. <u>ST</u> Do not get between a hippopotamus and its water or it might attack you.

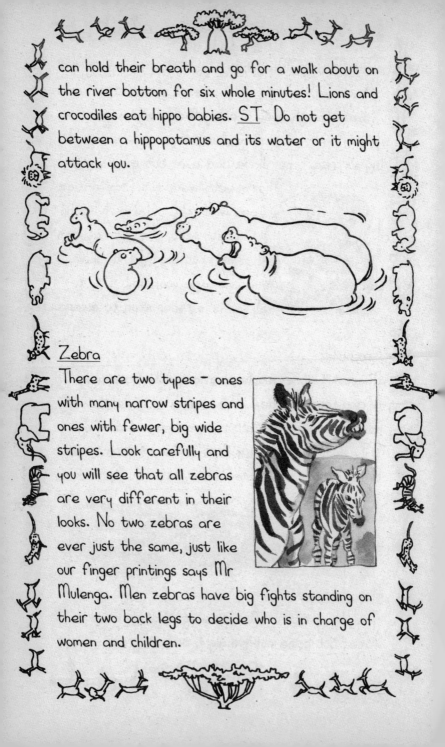

<u>Zebra</u>

There are two types – ones with many narrow stripes and ones with fewer, big wide stripes. Look carefully and you will see that all zebras are very different in their looks. No two zebras are ever just the same, just like our finger printings says Mr Mulenga. Men zebras have big fights standing on their two back legs to decide who is in charge of women and children.

Kudu

This is another sort of antelope - we make their horns into music instruments for blowing and bells to put on our cows.

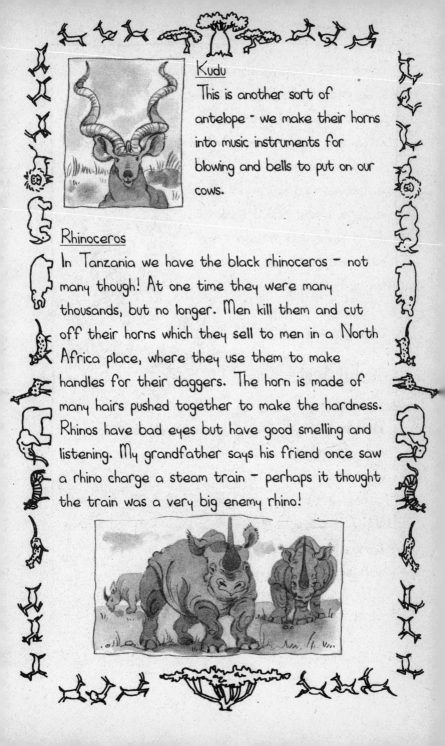

Rhinoceros

In Tanzania we have the black rhinoceros - not many though! At one time they were many thousands, but no longer. Men kill them and cut off their horns which they sell to men in a North Africa place, where they use them to make handles for their daggers. The horn is made of many hairs pushed together to make the hardness. Rhinos have bad eyes but have good smelling and listening. My grandfather says his friend once saw a rhino charge a steam train - perhaps it thought the train was a very big enemy rhino!

Some other tippings for you to be safe:

1. Do not sneak up on the animals and make them jump or they may attack you!

2. Do not make an animal feel trapped especially if it has babies.

3. Snakes and scorpions! When you are in the bush I think you should wear your trousers and socks and boots like I have seen the safari leaders do.

Beast wishes,

Christopher

PS Did you know that Maasai people do not normally kill wild animals? We let them have a good life like us.

And now I have also got a question for you! What is the animal that kills even more people in Africa than the crocodile?

Answer in my next letter.

25 May

Dear letter reader,

My safari trip is now finished and I am back home again. Since my returning I have been having a most interesting time because I have been finding about how you live. When the wazungu tourists had gone away and I was doing my safari camp tidying, I found some magazine paperbooks left behind. I have brought them back to my enkang. My eyes are popping out while I am looking at the coloured pictures of motor cars, swimming ponds, big houses and other amazing things, like living fishes inside boxes of glass and electrical toothybrushes!

Have you got things like these? And do you have rooms in your house with flushing toilets and toilet roll paper for your bottom? Nakordo says that in Europeland everyone has them. We do not have them at all where we are. We just go to a quiet place in the trees and use the leaves from the toilet bush for bottom wiping.

Another thing the tourists left for us was some food in tins. We have opened them and found them very interesting to taste, especially the worms which are in sauce. I think that they are called spaghettis? My brother says you have whole rooms full of food like this!

All of your freezing boxes and computers and washing up refrigerators and musical fi-his have got me completely surprised! You must be very, very clever to know how to mend these many machine things when they do not wish to work properly!

I cannot believe that you have so many things where you are! Your houses must be filled up so much that you cannot walk around inside them!

My big big brother said to me that many people throw stuffs away to make room for new buyings. He said that in many cities there are heaps of throwings away as big as a mountain! In Tanzania we do not do this at all. People are very poor so they use things very carefully and when they are worn away they use them for something else. When a tyre is no longer any good for a car we make it into some sandals. When an oil can is

old tyre

nice new sandals

It makes very nice music

oil can

empty we use it for a guitar body. Nakordo says that this is called recycling and now some of your countries are beginning to use this great idea of ours! He has told me that in some places in the West there are even big mountains of <u>thrown away food</u>! This makes me very sad indeed because in my country many, many little children go to bed starving hungry because we often do not have enough to eat here.

I think you are very, very lucky!

Big wishes,

Christopher

PS Have you got some garden gnomes? What are they for? Do you worship them?

Also . . . here is the answer to my last question:

The animal that kills more people in Africa than all the others is the <u>mosquito</u>!! Yes it is true! When this little insect bites you it can put a very bad illness into your body that may make you die. So make sure that you get a ~~job~~ jab before you come here!

2 June

Takwenya my friend with the bathpond room!

How is your flashing toilet? I have now returned to my school which has been made well again after the problems. Since I have been back I have been telling Mr Mulenga and the class about my interesting safari time with the wazungu. Mr Mulenga said it is a pity that they only have such a short time in Tanzania when there are so many wonderful things to see. We talked a bit about the great places of our country and he said to me, "Why don't you make a Tanzania touring guide for your pen friend?". So . . . here it is!

TANZANIA TOP TOUR ATTRACTIONS

THE RIFT VALLEY This big valley is many kilometres wide and with a flat bottom. It is thousands of kilometres long and goes almost all the way from the north to the south of Africa. It is also very deep in many places — about two kilometres! Yes . . . as high as five big skyscrapers buildings!

THE SERENGETI This is the biggest wildlife place in Africa and is also where my people lived. Then one day we were told to move away because this land was needed for wild animals and tourists. In Maa (our language) Serengeti means great open place with endless plains. There are millions of wildlife here.

THE NGORONGORO CRATER This is a giant bowl shape scooped out of the earth near to where I am living. It is very, very big inside! It used to be an enormous bubbling volcano, but then its middle bit sank down so it is now like a big empty dish full of grass and trees and water. It is more than half of a kilometre high from its top edge to its bottom floor.

The Maasai used to own it and lived inside it, but now we are not allowed to live there. It is needed for animals and tourists (yes, again!). 20,000 big wild animals live inside it now. There are many safari lodge hotels on the high edges so that the wazungu can watch the game beasts through their telescopes at breakfast then perhaps go for a safari drive inside it later on. We still take our cows to it for the grazing. Sometimes it is swarming everywhere with lions, elephants, wildebeest . . . and tourist mini-buses!

THE OLDUVAI GORGE This deep valley made from rock goes from the edge of the Ngorongoro crater to the Serengeti. It is a very important place for the whole world. A famous scientist found the bones and tools of the first ever human beings here. They were two million years old. The scientists also found footprints of very old people in volcano ash from nearly four million years ago.

MOUNT KILIMANJARO This amazing mountain is the biggest in Africa — nearly six kilometres to the top! It has got tropical jungles at its bottom but snow on its top all of the time! It is so big that you can see it from 160 kilometres away. Its bottom part covers a space bigger than all of Greatest London in the United Kingdom of Great

Britain! Many wazungu come to Tanzania to climb it. Kilimanjaro is a very old volcano which is just asleep, so it may one day explode again!

Once a leopard was found frozen dead right on top of it. It is not a place where they normally go and no one really knows why it went up there.

LAKE TANGANYIKA This great big lake is the deepest in Africa. It is nearly one-and-a-half kilometres deep. It is also very old – about 20 million years! It has got 250 different kinds of fish inside. Swimming cobra snakes live in the water and eat fish in the daytime. Then they slither on to the rocks and have a sleep at night.

Also at night time the Ha tribe fishermen go out in their boats. They wave lights at the type of little fish in the lake called dagga. When the dagga come up for a look at the lights, the fishing

men beat their drums very loud. This makes the fish go stiff with terror and the men scoop them up in their nets very fast.

You can see thousands of dagga

116

laid out on the shore being dried by the hot sun ready for eating.

ZANZIBAR This famous island was once a place for buying and selling people who had been captured for making into slaves. This terrible thing is not done here any more, thank goodness. It is also a place for growing spices, mainly ones called cloves. Do you eat them?

Some tourists like to come here to look at the very interesting buildings which were made for the rich slave-sellers in the old days. They also like to lie on top of the beach sand and do water swimming.

Plenty to see, you will agree!

Besty wishes,

Christopher

10 June

Dear writing friend,

Hello! Are you happy today? I hope you are! Here we are generally in a good feeling and looking forward to my brother's Eunoto ceremony in just a few days' time. It is a very important thing in his life and all of the junior warriors in his age group will go to it. Afterwards they will be very grown up senior warriors.

One little thing is making me feel sorry right now! My letters to you will certainly have to stop most soon. Remember I said that they would just be for one year and that is now almost gone away. Also Mr Mulenga is giving me more and more school work just recently. He thinks I am a clever brains boy and wants to help me become a top student. So, what with my cow work and another and one thing I will not have the time for more letters. I will be most sad to not talk to you any more.

Now for my news. I am having big problems with

118

a big crowd of hyenas who are sneaking about quite near to me and my cattle.

Do you know these creatures? They are like a very big dog, but are not a dog at all and are quite horrible to see. I have drawn you this picture of the ones which are troubling me and my cows.

They do not look nice, do they? Hyenas like to kill and eat antelopes and zebra, and cattle too! They are even dangerous for people. They sometimes take little children when they wander out from their enkang. Listen! If hyenas get their teeth into your body you are in <u>big</u> trouble! Their mouth is very, very strong and they can break up and swallow your bones no problem (they can do this with all the big animals, apart from elephants). They will try to swallow anything. My father has seen them eating old cattle sticks, thrown away shoes, bicycle seats . . . all sorts!

I often hear them doing their howls and screams

at night outside my enkang, especially when there is a big moon in the black sky. They also do a horrible laughing when they are happy at a kill — ha ha . . . ha ha — like that!! They live in holes under the ground and the woman hyena is the biggest one, not the man.

Yesterday the hyenas tried to steal the calf of my cow Mbilia but myself and my brave Nipa chased them off. Our big bull did put his horns into one and threw it high into the air, ha! I think I am quite forward looking to being back in my classroom tomorrow. School learning is much quieter than cow guarding!

Last thing. My father bought me my very own radio with some of the shillings from our safari work. It is my reward for helping him and I love it. It has a little winding handle which you turn to make it work when it becomes tired. I will listen to it when I am guarding my cattle! When I grow

up and get money from my job in the town I will have hundreds of radios and also live in a two storey house with four escalators! I cannot wait!

Best wishes,

Christopher

PS Do you have age group ceremonies like ours? I heard about your birthday parties? We do not take much notice of this thing in our life, ceremonies for whole age groups are much more important for us.

28 June

My dear best writing friend

I am now at my <u>very</u> last letter to you! Well, for the time being anyway. Maybe when I have been to college and got my top job I will start writing to you again, you never know! So that you will not be <u>too</u> sad I have put plenty into this one for you to enjoy.

For some days we have been having the ceremony of the Eunoto here and now all the young men of my brother's age group are senior warriors. There have been many people about and much, much activity. There was even a <u>fight</u>! I will now tell you about it all!

When the ceremony began there was big excitement in the air because it is a very important time in the young men's lives. They all looked magnificent and tall and strong with their heads and their bodies shining with red ochre and fat grease and their hair dangling in beautiful locks which they had spent much time plaiting and braiding for each other. It was all a real feast for my eyes and I hope this picture will give you some idea of its greatness!

As the warriors stamped and chanted their way past us children with much ringing of bells and blowing of kudu horns, I felt a very big need to be a brave warrior myself with my body covered in red paint and my big spear in my hand. I was completely overdone with excitement. I am telling you now that I wanted to fight a giant buffalo with my bare hands at that very moment! I was without fear at all and ready for anything!

But just then, my very little brother stood on a thorn and began to cry, so I had to pick him up and carry him to my mother and then the feeling was all gone.

When I got back the adamu jumping up and down dance was starting. The warriors had made their circle and soon they were all leaping high into the air with their two feet together and making fierce grunting noises and tossing of their heads, as if they had suddenly turned into ferocious lions! Here they are doing it. See how high they can go from their still standing take-off – I promise I have not pretended this bit at all!

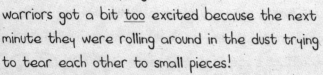

In between the dancings there was pushing and jostling and I think that two of the young warriors got a bit <u>too</u> excited because the next minute they were rolling around in the dust trying to tear each other to small pieces!

Luckily, after a moment or two some elders separated them and then they calmed down and made friends again.

After the dancing came the moment my big

brother was <u>not</u> looking forward to. The warriors
sat on stools and began unfastening the lovely hair
plaits that they had spent so much trouble doing.
Then, as they bent their
heads down with much
serious quietness, their
mothers came with their
razors and cut it all
away. Suddenly all over

the ground were the cut pieces of their hair!

My new bald-headed brother Leipo looked very
sad and I think I saw some tears mixing with
pattern paintings on his face. As well as his lovely
hair a whole good piece of his life had now gone
for ever. He was finished being a junior warrior.
His days of fun and adventures in the forest with
his warrior age group friends were over for good!

After the haircutting a bull was killed and
there was eating of the roasted meats. Then a

bit later on the young men
put white chalk on their
faces and went into the
ritual house. I am not sure
what happened in there as I
was not allowed to go in.

125

In a few years it will be time for me to become a junior warrior and learn to be very brave. I will make the most of this time and do much wandering in the bush and forest with much excitement and dangerous meetings. Of course, I will make sure I also fit in my school-going between my many adventures and explorations.

When I am doing these things I will think of you in your living place and wonder to myself if you are also having great adventures and excitement too.

Now, the time has come for me to finish this last letter to you. The dark is almost here and I can hardly no longer see my pieces of paper. As I am writing these very last words to you I can hear the hyenas cackling their

my last letter, how sad

horrible laughing just outside our thorn fence and I can also hear the coughing of a hunting leopard in the nearby bushes. It is making Nipa snarl his teeth and our calves are also getting quite restless inside their pen in my house. What noises are outside your house at this moment? Are they wild animal ones or just some things that I do not know about?

Anyway, I really must stop as I can hardly see a thing any more.

Bye for now.

Best wishes to you and your family and all of your cattle.

And may you always be stepping on cow poo.

Christopher ole Nerento

(Your best pal from Africa)

AIRMAIL FROM...

Would you like to read airmail letters
from children in other parts of the world?

Airmail From South East Asia - *Ban
Pong - where beetles taste great!* Shrimp
writes to you from Thailand, about food,
festivals, having fun Thai style, and lots
more. Meet Frog, her brother (*not* her
pet), and her funny Uncle Boon.

Airmail From South America -
Amazonia - where tree frogs go moo!
Maria and Leo are twins from
Copacabana in Brazil. They are going on
a brilliant adventure trip to the Amazon
Jungle, and they're writing to tell *you* all
about it.